QUESTIONS GALORE

Party Game Book™

SLEEPOVER EDITION

SADIE WORD

Published in 2019 by Sadie Word
Copyright Illustrations © 2019 by Nyx Spectrum
Printed in the United States of America

GREETINGS QUESTION SEEKERS!

Have you ever wanted to ride on the back of an Iguanodon dinosaur?

OR

Perhaps, you have been searching for a way to ask thought provoking questions to other humans for sport?

Well, this book can't help you with the Iguanodon until they come back from extinction, but it can help you start an engaging chat with other lifeforms!

This book is meant to inspire meaningful conversations with friends and family through oodles of thought provoking questions. Inspire loads of friendly inquiry with over 400 questions, enigmas, and conundrums!

So without any further ado, let the games begin!

DIRECTIONS:

Choose a reader.

Make sure to read the phrase, "Would you Rather-" at the beginning of each question.

The reader will read the first question and everyone will choose one of the choices given out loud.

Picking both or neither is not an option!

For the people who picked the least popular choice, ask them why they chose that?

You can also write the answers down on mini whiteboards, or make it into a points game!

PRO TIP:
Honestly, you really don't need to follow these directions. They have been included for those who like to follow the rules and need some boundaries. For all rule breaking rebels, please disregard these the direction pages and let pandemonium ensue!

Would you Rather?

Start off the slumber party
with laser tag
OR
A trip to the mall?

Tell scary stories around a bonfire
OR
Watch a scary movie in the dark?

Be a group of night owls
OR
Early birds?

Would you Rather?

Have a chick-flick movie marathon
OR
A Disney movie marathon?

Rock a pair of Emoji Poop slippers
OR
A pair of Cat slip-purrs?

Choreograph a dance to your favorite
boy band song
OR
Sing karaoke to your favorite
diva's song?

Would you Rather?

Make your own Cookie Pizza
OR
Have a Cupcake War competition?

Construct a pillow fort lined with
stuffed animals
OR
Build a blanket fort with string lights?

Play Guess Who with musicians
OR
YouTubers?

Would you Rather?

Tell everyone your future dreams and aspirations
OR
Admit that you are not sure what you want to do and ask your friends how they see future you?

Make friendship bracelets with the squad
OR
Make a secret handshake with the squad?

Would you Rather?

Make your own DIY cupcake lip balm
OR
DIY rainbow bath bombs?

Write inspirational notes to strangers
and leave them in library books
OR
Give a positive letter telling your
friend, "you got this" once a month?

Would you Rather?

Decorate pillowcases with your
friends' autographs
OR
Design your own eye mask with puffy
glitter paint?

Cuddle with a baby panda bear
OR
Cradle a cute koala bear?

Wear pink bunny slippers
OR
Slippers that look like giant yeti feet?

Would you Rather?

Make a giant cookie pizza
with your BFFs
OR
Each make your own individual
pizzas from scratch?

Make a dreamcatcher in the shape of a
crescent moon with blue feathers
OR
A dreamcatcher with a rainbow-
colored design with shimmering tassels
at the bottom?

Travel to Italy to see the Leaning Tower of Pisa and eat authentic pizza
OR
Go to London to have high tea and wave at the Queen of England?

Take selfies with a colored lens so you can have all of your pictures in your favorite color
OR
Take selfies with Polaroids that have rainbow borders around the image?

Would you Rather?

Wear cow slippers that moo every time you take a step

OR

Wear dinosaur slippers that roar every time you take a step?

Give a friend a
Unicorn Spa Jar DIY

OR

A DIY Unicorn sparkle slime jar?

Paint your own succulent planters

OR

Landscape your own fairy garden?

Would you Rather?

Go to the crafts store to get supplies for girls night
OR
Go to Bath & Body Works as your one-stop-shop for girls night?

Be captain of a pirate ship
OR
Be a pilot of a hot air balloon?

Donate your birthday gifts to charity
OR
Donate your hair to Locks for Love?

Would you Rather?

Wear cute narwhal slippers
OR
Pull off pink flamingo slippers?

Go north and see the Northern Lights
OR
Go out into the middle of the ocean to
see the Milky Way and all the stars?

Create a rainbow swirl tie-dye t-shirt
OR
Make a colorful geometric designed
colorshot tees?

Would you Rather?

Try out for a new sports team
OR
Audition for a part in a play with a
singing solo?

Have breakfast in bed
OR
Breakfast at noon?

Play flashlight tag all night long
OR
Spend the night playing charades?

Would you Rather?

Live 100 years in the future
OR
Live 100 years in the past?

Play M.A.S.H with your besties
OR
Play Mad Libs with your friends?

Watch a chick flick marathon
OR
Have a horror movie marathon?

Would you Rather?

Start a bullet journal for the year
OR
Start a diary and write in it once a day
for a year?

Make a pro and con list about all your
life decisions
OR
Decide your life decisions based on
your gut feeling?

Would you Rather?

Try making your own soap and experiment with uncommon scents
OR
Make your own lip gloss with unusual flavors?

Stay up until 5 in the morning at a sleepover and wake up when you have to leave
OR
Get up at 5 in the morning at a sleepover after some sleep and continue the party?

Would you Rather?

Go to Starbucks to get your
favorite Frappe
OR
Go to your favorite fast food
place for a snack?

Play two truths and one lie
with your BFFs
OR
Play the Sleeping Beauty Try Not
to Laugh Challenge?

Live in Hawaii, in paradise
OR
Live in your favorite city, metropolis?

Would you Rather?

Fly on the back of a Griffin
OR
Ride on the back of a Centaur?

Have an adventure with
Princess Jasmine
OR
Swim the seas with Princess Ariel?

Always have October weather
OR
Always have April weather?

Would you Rather?

Base your plans on the hourly weather forecast
OR
Make your plans dependent on your daily Horoscope?

Ride a horse on the beaches of Oregon
OR
Ride small horses to see Iceland's waterfalls and hot springs?

Explore the outback of Australia
OR
Wander the ancient streets of Rome?

Would you Rather?

Learn a new language
OR
Learn to cook food from another
culture?

Make an indoor floor maze with
construction paper
OR
Start a game of indoor ball toss with a
sand bucket and a Wiffle ball?

Would you Rather?

Go snorkeling at Great Barrier Reef
OR
Go skydiving in the
mountains of Switzerland?

Sleep in a hammock outside on the
beach while on vacation
OR
Go on safari and sleep in a treehouse?

Visit a medieval castle
OR
Go to the top of the Eiffel Tower?

Would you Rather?

Wear a beret for the next year
OR
Wear overalls for a whole year?

Only be able to play video games on the Game Boy Color
OR
Only have Virtual Reality games available to you?

Have real-life Pokémon
OR
Have a real-life Jurassic Park?

Would you Rather?

Bring back the typewriter
OR
Bring back the gramophone?

Light your entire house with
string lights
OR
Light your home with disco balls?

Go to Build-A-Bear Workshop
OR
See back to back movies on the IMAX?

Visit the island with wild horses
on the beach
OR
Go to the Kentucky Derby and
see the Thoroughbreds race?

Start a collection of geodes
OR
Start a collection of cute animal
erasers?

Would you Rather?

Ride in a helicopter and fly over
your favorite city
OR
Swim with dolphins in a
tropical paradise?

Fold a 1000 paper cranes and
make a wish
OR
Fill a whole mason jar of origami
stars you made?

Would you Rather?

Have a day off to be lazy and do whatever you want
OR
Have a day off to treat yourself to a day of hair, nails, and shopping?

Have a water balloon fight
OR
A laser tag party?

Visit every country in the world
OR
Visit every planet in space?

Would you Rather?

Make a duct tape wallet that you use
for the next 7 years
OR
A whole duct tape dress that you try to
wear out in public 7 times?

Have a fiesta complete with nachos,
guac, and tacos
OR
Have a tea party with tiny cakes, tea,
and finger sandwiches?

Would you Rather?

Take pictures with your besties all
night long in the photo-booth
OR
Make a secret handshake and
friendship bracelets for each other?

Put on a fashion show with your Mom's
old clothes
OR
Put on a fashion show with old
Halloween costumes?

Would you Rather?

Have the perfect breakfast of unlimited donuts of all kinds
OR
The most fabulous breakfast ever of pink princess pancakes with rainbow glitter syrup?

Bring back the Unicorn Frappuccino
OR
Bring back the dinosaurs?

Would you Rather?

Have a mermaid pool party
in the summer
OR
Have a cozy unicorn glow-in-the-dark
party in the winter?

Write fairy tale stories for each other
OR
Pretends to be their favorite Disney
Princess for the rest of the night?

Wear matching cat-ear headbands
all night long
OR
Give each other blind hair-dos?

Make your own flower crown from
wildflowers
OR
Buy a flower crown of fake roses in
rainbow colors?

Would you Rather?

Draw your dreams on rainbow
scratch-off paper
OR
Reenact your dreams in funny
videos with friends?

Have s'mores waffles in the morning
OR
Have funfetti pancakes in the morning?

Would you Rather?

Make tents in the living room and have a glamping party next to the fireplace
OR
Go camping at a state park with the girl scout troop and learn to survive in the wilderness?

Wear matching pajamas with your BFF
OR
Have matching slippers and hairdos with your BFF?

Would you Rather?

Always have to tell the truth when
asked a question
OR
Always have to do the chicken
dance when you lie?

Dare to play Beanboozled
with your BFFs
OR
Play spin the nail polish bottle with
dares on the board?

Would you Rather?

Have your sleepover Moto be:
"llamaste in bed all day"
OR
"morning hair, don't care"?

Change your hairstyle
OR
Change your clothing style?

Rock some poop emoji slippers
OR
Sleep on a princess poop emoji pillow?

Would you Rather?

Bake brownies before bed
OR
Snack on cookie dough before bed?

Decorate your sleepover
with lava lamps
OR
Glow-in-the-dark stars and
constellations?

Make arts and crafts with your besties
OR
Make all your favorite foods
with your BFFs?

Would you Rather?

Let your Dad paint your nails with his own design
OR
Paint your Dad's toes with hot pink glitter nail polish?

Adopt a teacup pig
OR
Adopt a hedgehog as your future pet?

Do your part by donating to charities
OR
Start your own charity for a cause you are passionate about?

Would you Rather?

Work hard and finally have your dream
job when you're 35
OR
Start your own business in your
20's and be your own boss at
your dream job?

Use a fanny pack that looks like your
belly is hanging out of your shirt
OR
Use an empty to-go coffee cup to hold
everything your purse would?

Would you Rather?

Live the rest of your days in
a Red Wood tree
OR
Live the rest of your days in a cave?

Only be able to communicate in text
messages with emojis
OR
Only be able to communicate with
others in person without talking
and only using your own facial
expressions?

Would you Rather?

Make your BFF laugh by making funny faces and gestures
OR
By making constant corny puns and dad jokes?

Go rollerskating at a retro rink with an 80s theme
OR
Go ice skating in old fashioned clothing from the 1920's?

Have a High School Musical marathon
OR
Binge-watch all of Glee?

What's on your phone?

1 POINT

- ☐ Selfie
- ☐ Instagram App
- ☐ Game App
- ☐ Alarm Clock that's on
- ☐ Weather App

5 POINTS

- ☐ Pet as your background
- ☐ Battery Life is >20%
- ☐ Contact name starts with "J"
- ☐ Music App
- ☐ Case with cute design

10 POINTS

- ☐ More than 50 Contacts
- ☐ Missed Call Notification
- ☐ Ringtone is a Song
- ☐ Sunset Photo
- ☐ Video with BFF

15 POINTS

- ☐ 90s Boy Band Album
- ☐ Over 1,000 Photos
- ☐ Battery Life is < 90
- ☐ Zero Notifications on any app
- ☐ Texts with an Elderly Relative

500 POINTS

- ☐ I don't have a phone

TIEBREAKER

- ☐ I don't have a tablet

Most likely to...

Directions:

The oldest person in the room gets to read first.

Make sure to read the phrase, "Who would be the most likely to-" at the beginning of each question.

Read a question and have everyone (including the reader) point at the person in the room that best fits the statement.

The person who has the most people pointing at them gets the point and also gets to read the next question.

Continue this until someone gets 10 points or (if you're having too much fun) you run out of questions!

Most likely to...

Do their own stunts?

End up on the red carpet someday?

End up on the red carpet someday?

Become a Food Critic?

Be on an episode of Jeopardy?

Most likely to...

Be the millionaire that somebody marries?

Be the Master of Wii Sports?

Become the old person yelling at kids to get off their lawn?

Get married first?

Most likely to...

Become a teacher?

Get ID'd when they're 30?

Break a world record in a strange category?

Be caught sleeping during class?

Most likely to...

Participate in an Extreme Unicycling Race?

Given the title Knitter-in-Residence?

Live on your couch in the future?

Find a way to go back in time?

Most likely to...

Write a best selling book?

Get famous with a funny
social media post?

Coach Little League Baseball?

Become a Master Chef?

Most likely to...

Chug a bottle of hot sauce like it's nothing?

Become a Vampire?

Grow up to be a "Parkour Specialist"?

Be remembered by others as that "Cool Kid"?

Most likely to...

Legally change their name
to Tara Dactyl?

Start a blog and make bank
on random posts?

Give others unwanted advice?

Be the most sparkly human ever?

Most likely to...

Never know what is going on but is always game for whatever it is?

Slowly draining your bank account into extinction?

Fix everything with duct tape or bobby pins?

Have morning hair like Einstein?

Most likely to...

Become the Hulk if kept up too late?

Be renamed "Sleeping Beauty" because once they fall asleep, you can't wake them up?

Volunteer at an animal shelter?

Most likely to...

Become a sports fan who wears cheese on their head...willingly?

Be a future Olympian?

Be everyone's shoulder to cry on?

Be the ultimate unsung hero?

Most likely to...

Move out of the country?

Wear their slippers to school?

Try to crawl around like a caterpillar
in their sleeping bag?

Only have matching pajamas in their
wardrobe?

Most likely to...

Try to scare younger siblings while wearing a facial mask?

Sleep with their ballet shoes on?

Talk in their sleep?

Photobomb everyone's selfies?

Most likely to...

Fail a prank call because they're too polite?

Know every word to the movies you will watch later?

Wake up looking like they already spent two hours putting themselves together?

Most likely to...

Open their noisy candy bag at the quietest part of the movie?

Have the most alarms on their phone to get them up for school?

Have a phone screen that looks more like a rectangular spider web then an actual phone?

Be that person who always calls you instead of just texting you?

Most likely to...

Have the forbidden power of always looking good in every single photo ever taken of them?

Have the best laugh that is funnier than the jokes others tell?

Be the Squad's Sass Master?

Be the Mom of the group?

Most likely to...

Be the friend who is always dancing, even in her sleep?

Always have the final decision in the group on what everyone is doing?

Make the squad try new things and go on adventures?

Be the friend who brutally honest, and you can go to get advice from?

Be the quiet one, who may not speak a lot, but is a valued part of the squad?

Be the crazy one who is equally lovable as they is wacky, and makes the room laugh?

Be the person who knows it all, and should legally change their name to "Siri"?

What's in your Overnight Bag?

1 POINT

- ☐ Toothbrush
- ☐ Hair Brush
- ☐ Nail Polish
- ☐ Floss
- ☐ Hair Ties

5 POINTS

- ☐ Silly Slippers
- ☐ Headphones
- ☐ Pillow
- ☐ Sleepover Playlist or CD
- ☐ Clothes for the next day

10 POINTS

- ☐ Stuffed Animal
- ☐ Makeup
- ☐ Matching Pajamas
- ☐ Flashlight
- ☐ Funny Socks

15 POINTS

- ☐ Favorite Game
- ☐ Headband
- ☐ Sleeping Mask
- ☐ Camera or Phone
- ☐ Something Glittery

TIEBREAKER

- ☐ Favorite Movie dvd

Directions:

Don't Get Me Started is a funny twist on the
Try Not to Laugh Challenge.

The group will choose one of the following topics
for the first person to perform a rant.

The person destined to rant may do one of
two things. They can either have an angry,
heated rant about the topic. Or they can
have an excited, and hysterical rant about
the subject like it's the only thing
they've ever loved!
Trust me, both are a hoot.

The ranting person must keep up their performance
until they have everyone in the room laughing.

Take turns until everyone has done at least one rant!

Parades

Sloths

School Buses

Mimes

DON'T GET me STARTED!

Pineapples

Garden Gnomes

Fried Chicken

Clowns

DON'T GET me STARTED!

Peanut Butter and Fluff Sandwiches

Justin Bieber

Shark Week

Chick-fil-A

DON'T GET me STARTED!

The Jonas Brothers are reunited!

Fidget Spinners

Mermaid Tails

Fortnite

DON'T GET me STARTED!

Poop Emoji or Ice Cream Emoji?

Flippy Sequins

Avocado Toast

Cat Ear Headbands

DON'T GET ME STARTED!

Owls

Donuts

Horses

Llamas

DON'T GET me STARTED!

Farting Coloring Books

The Eiffel Tower

Strawberry Toothpaste

Canadian Geese

DON'T GET me STARTED!

People who believe Giraffes are from Mars

Music Snobs

Mushrooms

Lack of Dragons in all movies

DON'T GET me STARTED!

Pumpkin Spice Lattes

Pillow Fights

Fainting Goats

How everything is a Unicorn now

DON'T GET me STARTED!

Ugg Boots

Roombas

Misspelled Signs

Only having 2 hours of sleep

DON'T GET me STARTED!

Angry Birds

Car Commercials

Football

Garlic Ice Cream

DON'T GET me STARTED!

Yodeling Pickles

Drinking water with a minty mouth

The song "Let it Go"

Fanny Packs

DON'T GET me STARTED!

Pineapple on Pizza

Avocado Bath Bombs

Stepping on Legos

Watch Ya' Mouth Videos

DON'T GET me STARTED!

Making yourself into a Blanket Burrito

Nightgowns

Koi Fish

Succulents

DON'T GET me STARTED!

Ninjas

Caticorns

Zebra Print

Queen Elizabeth's Corgis

Selfie
SCAVENGER HUNT

- ☐ Pink Slippers

- ☐ Something Orange

- ☐ Nail Polish bottles arranged in the order of the rainbow

- ☐ Someone else pretending to sleep

- ☐ 3 Stuffed Animals in a sleeping bag

- ☐ Junk Food for the party

- ☐ Something that glows-in-the-dark

☐ A Unicorn

☐ Sleeping Mask

☐ Balloons

☐ Someone in a Onesie

☐ Something Chocolate

☐ String lights

☐ Something Purple

☐ Photo Booth with a funny prop

☐ Someone in a bathrobe

Truth OR Dare!

Directions:

Let the shortest person start as the reader.

The reader will ask the person to their left
the question, "Truth or Dare"?

The person who is asked "Truth or Dare" will decide
whether they want to answer a Truth Question or
perform a Dare. You cannot change your mind after
choosing Truth or Dare.

All Truth questions will be found on the left pages.
AND
All Dares will be found on the right pages.

When that person has completed their Truth or Dare,
the reader will then pass the book to the person
on their right.

Truth OR Dare!

Warning!

You cannot lie when you choose a Truth question.
AND
No matter what the dare is, you have to do it.

The Truth questions are designed to have everyone
share something little known about themselves.
AND
The Dares are designed to challenge the person
attempting them, not to embarrass them.

If needed: Set a time limit for how long a person has
to complete the Truth or Dare.

TRUTH

Have you ever talked
in your sleep?

Do you sneak sweets when the
parents aren't looking?

What was your last
dream about?

DARE

Have the person to your left put lipstick on you...blindfolded.

Play the rest of the game using a funny accent.

Do 15 pushups.

TRUTH

What is your favorite book?

Would you go to school in a SpongeBob costume for $20?

Do you sleep with a stuffed animal?

DARE

Crabwalk to the bathroom, turn around and come back to the game. Greet anyone along the way with, "Ahoy, there!"

Eat a spoonful of sugar.

Act like a monkey for the next three turns.

TRUTH

Is there something in your life you wish you could redo? What would it be?

Do you sleep with a nightlight?

Where is the one place you really want to travel someday?

DARE

Attempt to juggle with three stuffed animals.

Make your best impression of a Disney Princess. Keep doing it until someone has guessed who you are.

Wear your slippers on your hand for the next two turns.

TRUTH

If you could be any animal, what would you be?

Have you ever been compared to another person? If so, who?

What is the best thing that has happened to you this week?

DARE

Take a selfie, while the rest of the party tries to photobomb you.

Prank call: Call Domino's Pizza and ask them for Pizza Hut's number.

Talk like a snobby British man for the rest of the game.

TRUTH

If you could be someone else for one day, who would it be, and what would you do?

What is your favorite time of year?

Do you keep a diary/journal/ sketchbook?

DARE

Sing the ABCs backwards.

Do the Macarena sitting down for five minutes.

Draw a mustache on yourself, without a mirror.

TRUTH

What would you do with $10,000?

Have you ever fed a pet your dinner under the table?

If you could be a vegetable, what would it be?

Grab a hairbrush and use it as a microphone. Pretend to be a Show Host and commentate on the next person's turn.

Smell everyone's breath and guess what they ate last.

Pretend you are a chicken for the next two turns.

TRUTH

If you could be in a cartoon, which cartoon would you be in?

What was the most expensive thing you have ever broke?

What superpower would you want to have? Why that power?

Tell everyone what tomorrow's weather forecast is, but pretend you are a malfunctioning robot while doing it.

Give us instructions on how to make a peanut butter and jelly sandwich while talking like a pirate.

Do a silly walk around the room until you find an item that starts with the letter "K."

TRUTH

Using only what you had around you right now, would you survive the zombie apocalypse?

If you are what you eat, what are you?

What item would you grab first if your house was on fire?

Challenge someone to a staring contest. Whoever blinks first must wear their PJs inside out for the rest of the game.

Make your best evil laugh anytime someone says the word "sleepover" for the rest of the game.

Do your best moonwalk across the room.

TRUTH

What kind of dragon are you?

Would you go back in time or travel to the future? Why?

Would you be friends with your parents if they were the same age as you?

Pretend to hula hoop while singing "Twinkle Twinkle Little Star."

Say "Seashells" 10 times fast without messing up. Repeat until you can say it 10 times in a row.

Tell us the story of how you met your new friend Jerry the Kangaroo, in your best caveman voice.

TRUTH

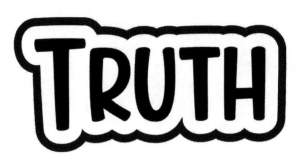

What is your superhero name?

What mythical creature do you wish was real?

What do you think could change the world?

Try to do the wave with your eyebrows.

Grab the nearest stuffed animal and use it as a fashion item. Do your best runway walk with it and pose three times.

Try to lick your elbow while singing, "I'm a Little Teapot."

TRUTH

What is your motto for life?

What is the funniest face you can make?

If you were to run a business, what kind of business would it be?

Balance a spoon on your nose
for 10 seconds.

Try to keep a straight face while
everyone else in the room tries
to get you to laugh without
touching you. If you laugh, you
must spend the rest of the game
talking like Patrick Star.

Name the Seven Dwarves.

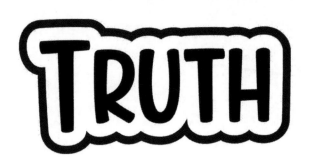

TRUTH

What is your favorite restaurant to have dinner at?

What scares you the most?

What is the longest word you know?

Go a whole minute without blinking.

Pretend you are 90 years old for the next five minutes.

Do the best impersonation of someone you know. Keep doing it until someone guesses who you are.

TRUTH

What is a chore you don't mind doing?

What would your dream house look like?

If you could rename yourself, what name would you pick?

Try to roll your tongue into the shape of a three-leaf clover.

Do 25 jumping jacks.

Yodel the chorus of your favorite song.

TRUTH

What's your favorite kind of cookie?

If you could play any musical instrument, what would it be?

What Disney Princess would you share your room with?

DARE

Let someone tickle you for 30 seconds.

Quick! Play dead for the next 2 minutes!

Try to do a split. Go as far as you can go and yell, "Tada"!

TRUTH

Do you prefer to be indoors or outdoors?

What's your secret talent?

What is your favorite ice cream flavor?

Give someone a mighty
bear hug.

Do a belly-dance while everyone
sings "Yankee Doodle."

Try to touch your nose with
your tongue.

TRUTH

Is there a sport or after school activity that you have always wanted to try?

Who is your favorite singer or band?

What never fails to make you laugh?

DARE

Play Hide and Seek, but everyone has to count and then come and find you!

Give a foot massage to the person on your right.

Let the group give you a new hairstyle that you have to wear for the rest of the game.

SWEET DREAM HOROSCOPES

ARIES (MARCH 21 – APRIL 19)

You will dream of birds.
Birds symbolize transformation and freedom from limitations. Birds appear as messengers to you and will offer you wisdom and insight. Trust yourself and soar into your future.

TAURUS (APRIL 20 – MAY 20)

You will dream of games.
Games in dreams symbolize how you approach life. The board game reveals the moves you make through life. Focus on your strategy, and continue your path to prosperity.

GEMINI (MAY 21 – JUNE 20)

You will dream of a famous person.
The famous person is in your dream to express the type of recognition you wish for. They may also represent a part of your personality that you are holding back from the world. Don't be afraid to bring your true self into the spotlight.

CANCER (JUNE 21 – JULY 22)

You will dream of gemstones.
Pay attention to the color of the gems
in your dreams. They might be the
color of your birthstone, or of
someone else's birthstone, who is
close to you. Keep the stone close, it
will protect you and help you shine
when you need a little extra courage.

LEO (JULY 23 – AUG 22)

You will dream of fruit.
Fruit in your dreams means you are going
through a time of personal growth. If the
fruit is not yet ripened, it suggests failed
attempts to achieve a goal. But don't give
up! Like a fruit tree, there is always more
than one fruit growing at a time. You will
have plenty of opportunities to reach
your goal.

VIRGO (AUG 23 – SEPT 22)

You will dream of music.
Hearing music in your dreams is a positive
thing. Music heals the soul and suggests that
you are in tune with your inner harmony.
Take note of the song and its mood. That
song will reflect what you're really feeling.
Continue to listen and make sure you stay in
tune with yourself.

LIBRA (SEPT 23 — OCT 22)
You will dream of wildflowers.
Wildflowers represent freedom, and the natural beauty everyone is born with. This natural garden is an indication that you will be happier if you go with the flow and stop worrying about the order of things. Let go of your doubts and be free to flourish!

SCORPIO (OCT 23 — NOV 21)
You will dream of dragons.
Dreaming of dragons is neither good nor bad. The dragon is the symbol of the universal energy that flows through everything. If the dragon can breathe fire, it is a symbol of your inner strength and how you will soon overcome your doubts.

SAGITTARIUS (NOV 22 — DEC 21)
You will dream of sports.
Are you ahead of your opponents, or in need of catching up? Your dreams are trying to show you how you are progressing in life. Make sure to defeat your competitors honestly, and with fair play. That is the recipe for happiness.

CAPRICORN (DEC 22 – JAN 19)

You will dream of the Earth.
Lying down on the Earth represents you need to become more grounded. You should focus on your tasks in real life, and not get lost in the fantasy of daydreams. Take time to focus on yourself and what you are doing.

AQUARIUS (JAN 20 – FEB 18)

You will dream of fish.
It is a legendary instinct to dream of fish swimming around you. They represent your home and family, who will always present in your life, no matter how far you swim. Keep working towards your goals and just keep swimming!

PISCES (FEB 19 – MARCH 20)

You will dream in a foreign language.
Unknown languages are symbols of good luck, they represent a part of yourself that you do not yet fully understand. Like any skill, it takes practice and patience to understand a new language. Keep listening to yourself, in time, you will understand.

NEVER HAVE I EVER...

Directions:

Let the person with the longest hair,
read the first page of questions.

Make sure to read the phrase, "Never have I ever-"
at the beginning of each question.

Anyone who can answer "yes, I have done this
thing you speak of" to the question gets a point.

The first person to get to 15 points wins!

Other fun ways to play:
Snacking Game - Everyone is given 10 to 20 sweets.
Whoever runs out of sweets first, wins!

Pro tip:
This version is best played with small
snacks like popcorn, jellybeans, M&Ms, etc.

And for those who have already snacked:

Ten Fingers Game - Everyone holds up all ten fingers.
If you can say "yes" to any of these statements,
you put down one finger. The first one
to put down all their fingers wins!

NEVER HAVE I EVER...

Broken a bone?

Recorded myself singing?

Been on TV?

Have a secret social media account?

NEVER HAVE I EVER...

Skipped class?

Ridden in a limo?

Watched every Shrek movie?

Followed the Big Ben clock on Twitter?

NEVER HAVE I EVER...

Kept a plant alive?

Ate dessert before dinner?

Had a nightmare about something chasing me?

Tried something I saw on Pinterest?

NEVER HAVE I EVER...

Stayed up all night without any sleep the next day?

Followed a makeup tutorial on YouTube?

Traveled outside of the country?

Gone horseback riding?

NEVER HAVE I EVER...

Read an entire book in one day?

Broke your phone or tablet?

Danced in the rain?

Played Five Nights at Freddy's?

NEVER HAVE I EVER...

Won a sports game?

Gone swimming in the ocean?

Made a blanket fort that covered an entire room?

Baked cookies at midnight?

NEVER HAVE I EVER...

Pretended to sleep to fool
your parents?

Slept in a tent?

Finished a game of Monopoly?

Followed one of the Muppets
on Twitter?

NEVER HAVE I EVER...

Played video games all night long?

Gone to a real spa?

Carved a watermelon like a jack-o-lantern?

Held a lizard?

NEVER HAVE I EVER...

Sang karaoke in public?

Asked Siri "What is zero divided by zero"?

Gone to a farm with animals?

Taught a dog how to do a trick?

NEVER HAVE I EVER...

Had a drink out of a coconut?

Photoshopped a photo I took?

Wore matching pajamas with your family?

Posted a picture without a filter?

NEVER HAVE I EVER...

Played a never-ending game of UNO and gave up?

Read all the Harry Potter books?

Cut your hair for charity?

Went out in public in an animal onesie?

NEVER HAVE I EVER...

Had flavored syrup on pancakes?

Had a pillow fight?

Been in a food coma from junk food?

Embraced your morning hair and went to school without touching it?

NEVER HAVE I EVER...

Guessed who the correct villain was in an episode of Scooby-Doo?

Danced the floss?

Stayed in pajamas all day long?

Looked under your bed for a monster when you were little?

NEVER HAVE I EVER...

Tried Sugar Cookie flavored tea?

Fallen asleep first at a sleepover?

Gone swimming in a lake?

Been on an airplane?

THANK YOU!

You are the most marvelous person for purchasing this book, thank you!

Congratulations on adopting this charming little edition into your home library! If it has brought you even a thimble full of joy, please consider leaving a review for it on Amazon.com

I shall wait patiently for your comments, my dear readers. Any guidance you are willing to bestow unto me helps me take another step closer to becoming the Grand Poobah of Game Books.

Help the cause, start a trend, and write a review!

-Sadie Word

Also by Sadie Word:

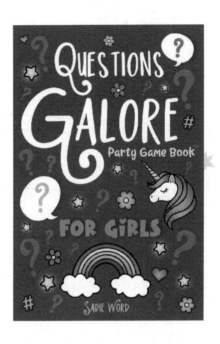

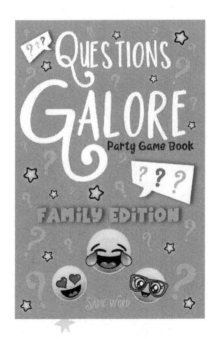

Also by Nyx Spectrum:

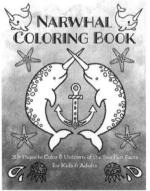

Made in the USA
Columbia, SC
08 June 2020